Look and Find®

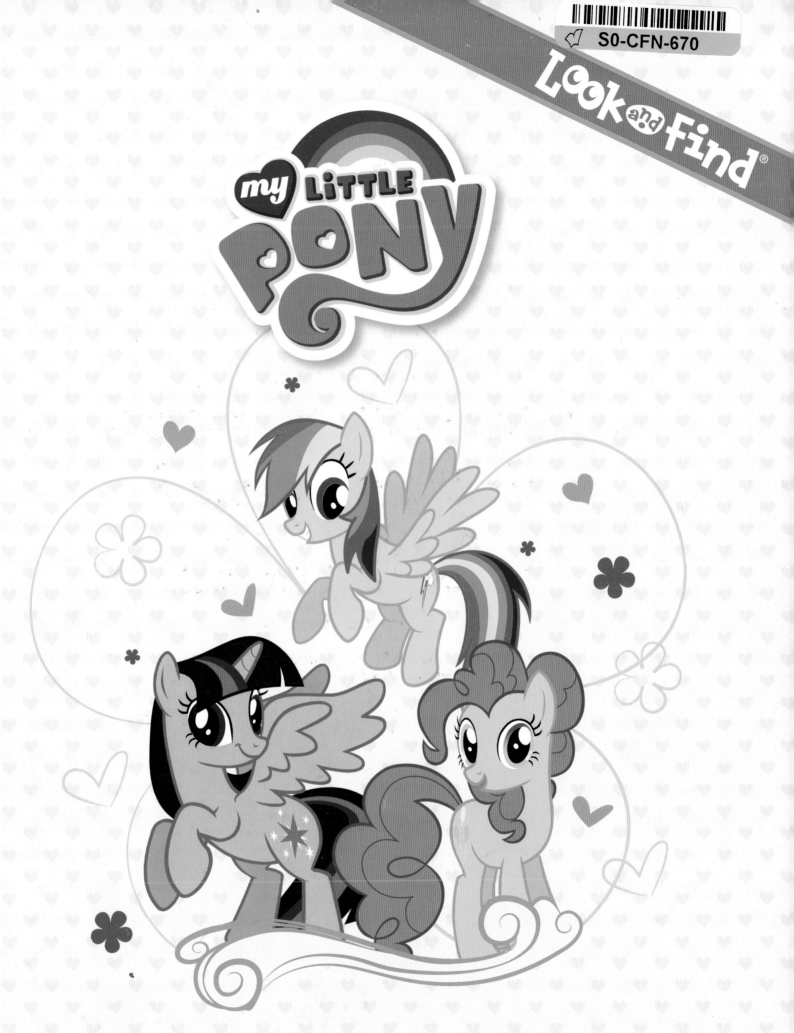

phoenix international publications, inc.

Welcome to Ponyville! On their walk through town, Twilight Sparkle, Pinkie Pie, and their friends are keeping an eye out for familiar landmarks. Can you spot them, too?

horseshoes

street sign

mailbox

apple barrel

wishing well

street lamp

Twilight Sparkle is reading about the magic of friendship. While she studies, look for these books:

Rainbow Dash is practicing her sonic rainboom! Use your finger to trace her path through Cloudsdale starting from her home:

Start Here

Applejack knows apples. That's why she's in charge of food for every party! Look around and find these treats made with apples:

apple tart

apple cupcake

apple pudding

apple slice

baked apple

apple pie

Fluttershy can fly because she has wings. Can you find these flying friends?

Rainbow Dash

bumblebee

bluebird

this flutterfly

this butterfly

green bird

dragonfly

Pinkie Pie loves to make the treats sold at SugarCube Corner. See if you can find these sugary sweets:

berry cake

cherry pie

lollipop

this cupcake

this taffy cream

doughnut

Everypony has a favorite shampoo. Can you find these shampoo bottles while Rarity enjoys her weekly trip to the spa?

It looks like everypony in Canterlot is a guest at the coronation of Twilight Sparkle! Find these ponies (and one dragon!) whose friendship helped Twilight earn her tiara:

Rarity

Rainbow Dash

Spike

Fluttershy

Pinkie Pie

Applejack

Ponyville is full of love! Stroll back through town and count all the hearts ♥ you can find. Do you see 6, 8, or 10?

The Library has many colorful stories to tell. Turn back and see if you can find something that is:

yellow

pink

red

green

blue

purple

white

Soar back to the sky with Rainbow Dash and look for these shapes among the clouds:

star

triangle

horseshoe

heart

clover

circle

Ponies love to eat healthy food. Trot back to Sweet Apple Acres and see if you can find these fruits and vegetables:

bananas

carrots

celery

pears

strawberries

grapes

pineapple

corn

Flutterfly has lots of animal friends! Fly back to the meadow and find things that start with each letter of the word FRIENDS:

F - frog

R - rabbit

I - inchworm

E - egg

N - nest

D - duck

S - squirrel

Pinkie Pie rhymes with Fluttershy! Help Pinkie Pie work on her next sweet song by searching SugarCube Corner for things that rhyme with these words:

cat (hat)

fly (pie)

sing (wing)

hug (rug)

moon (spoon)

shell (bell)

Spa begins with the letter s. Step back to the spa to find these items that start with s, too:

sponge	slippers
sunglasses	stool
soap	sandals

Count a lot in Canterlot! Find and count these things at Twilight's coronation:

1	ice-cream cone	4	tiaras
2	bells	5	balloons
3	birds	6	streamers